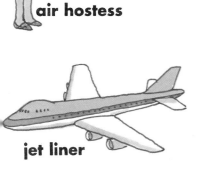
dinghy

seaweed

coach

baggage
trolley

water bottle

arrot

drink

hat

air hostess

jet liner

# MY STORY WORD BOOK OF
# GOING ON HOLIDAY

©1995 GRANDREAMS LIMITED

Published by Grandreams Limited,
Jadwin House, 205/211 Kentish Town Road,
London, NW5 2JU.

Printed in China.

safari jacket

binoculars

spade

bucket

video camera

sunbed

flippers

starfish

downhill
racer

"We'll pack the case!" cried Susie and Tom.

"I'll ring Grandpa and Grandma and ask them to look after Monty," suggested Dad.

"Come on," said Mum "first I need to buy lots of new clothes!"

# Monty will need ...

dog basket

tinned food

box

biscuits

food bowl

water bowl

blanket

brush

comb

squeaky toy

rubber bone

rubber ring

collar

lead

# A visit to the travel agent

When the Cherry family decide to go on a holiday Dad said, "Let's visit the travel agent."
"I can show you some holidays on the computer." said the lady at the desk.

brochures

world map

poster

shelves

calendar

computer

keyboard

telephone

calculator

stapler

carpet

desk

"If we are going on holiday for two weeks, we will need some new luggage!" said Mum.

hold-all

backpack

camera bag

beauty case

flight bag

basket

'Don't forget to take your sunglasses and lots of sun-cream!'

travel bag

rucksack

luggage trolley

# Tom wants to go on safari

Each member of the family got lots of brochures on where they would like to go. "Let's go on safari," cried Tom, "and see all the wild animals."

bush hat

safari jacket

binoculars

water bottle

video camera

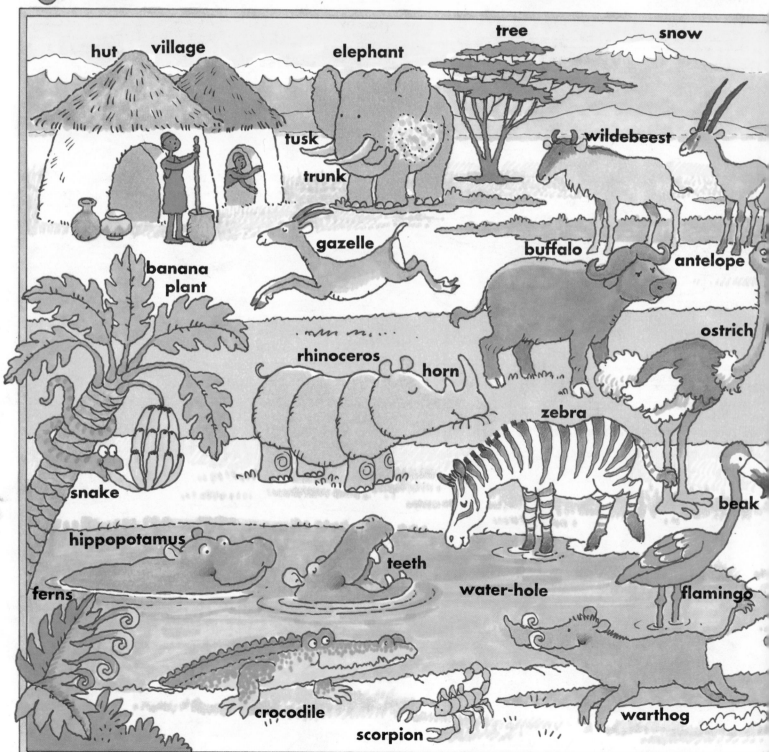

hut   village   elephant   tree   snow

tusk

trunk

wildebeest

gazelle

buffalo

antelope

banana plant

ostrich

rhinoceros   horn

zebra

snake

beak

hippopotamus

teeth

water-hole

flamingo

ferns

crocodile

scorpion

warthog

hornbill

chimpanzee

cheetah

scorpion

bananas

butterfly

parrot

clay pots

ant

lion cub

python

mountains

giraffe

bush helmet

leopard

spear

vehicle

spare wheel

native guide

tyre tracks

elephant calf

bill

hyena

lion

ant-hill

anteater

tongue

plants

lioness

# Mum wants to go skiing

"I have always wanted to learn to ski," said Mum.
"We could go on holiday in the snowy mountains. That would be great fun!"

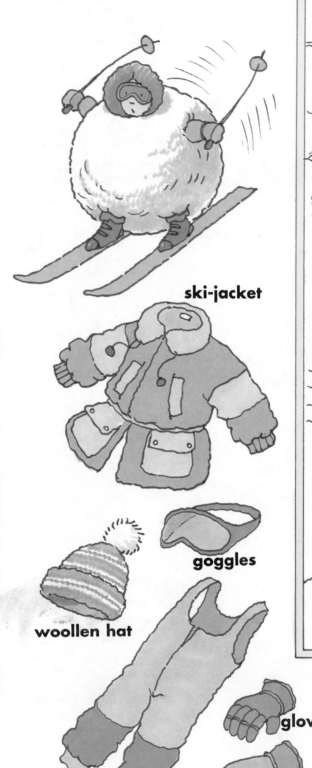

ski-jacket

goggles

woollen hat

ski-suit

glove

mitt

peak

avalanche

cable-car

chalet

pylon

forest

chair lift

bobsleigh team

skier

snowman

snow-plough

flag

downhill racer

finish

ski-boots

helmet

roof-ra

jeep

cable

ski-jump

church

ski-lodge

hotel

hood

anorak

instructor

slope

snowmobile

snowblower

marker flag

ski

ski-stick

fir-tree

snow

# Susie wants to go camping

"We could all have a wonderful time living in tents. We could cook outdoors and sail our rubber dingy," laughed Susie. "It's a camping holiday for me!"

kettle

matches

tent-peg

camping stove

folding stool

fish

pine trees

boulders

waterfall

bridge

stream

lake

rowing-boat

house-boat

dog

hiking boots

grass

litter basket

squirrel

raccoon

litter

mug

heavy rucksack

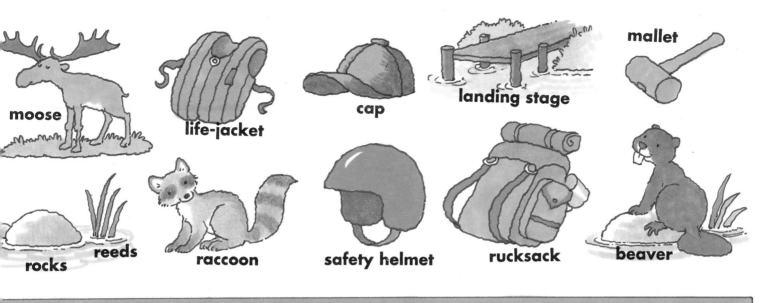

moose

life-jacket

cap

landing stage

mallet

rocks

reeds

raccoon

safety helmet

rucksack

beaver

smoke

fisherman

mobile home

log cabins

bear

rubber dinghy

tent

frying-pan

canoe

picnic basket

fishing rod

paddle

# Dad would love a coach tour

"I would like to relax the minute my holiday begins!" said Dad Cherry.
"How about a coach tour through different countries?"

roof

cloud

castle

town hall

barge

cruise ship

coach

hotel sign

umbrella

street sweeper

backpack

map

cobbles

table

waiter

policeman

tourists

photographer

violin

tuba

trumpet

clarinet

flower basket

cruise ship

window box

hotel sign

drinks

tray

sports car

bell tower

clock

tiles

tram wires

river

banner

flower stall

tram

tram rails

brass band

baskets

musician

music stand

coach driver

courier

passengers

barge

camera

tripod

coach

road signs

# A taxi to the station

At last the Cherry family agreed on a holiday in the sun.

On the morning of the holiday Grandpa and Grandma came round very early to collect Monty the dog, he was having his holiday with them.

Soon a taxi arrived to take the family to the station.

"I've never been in a train before!" said Tom. "Neither have I!" laughed Susie.

"Wait until you see the airport," smiled Dad.

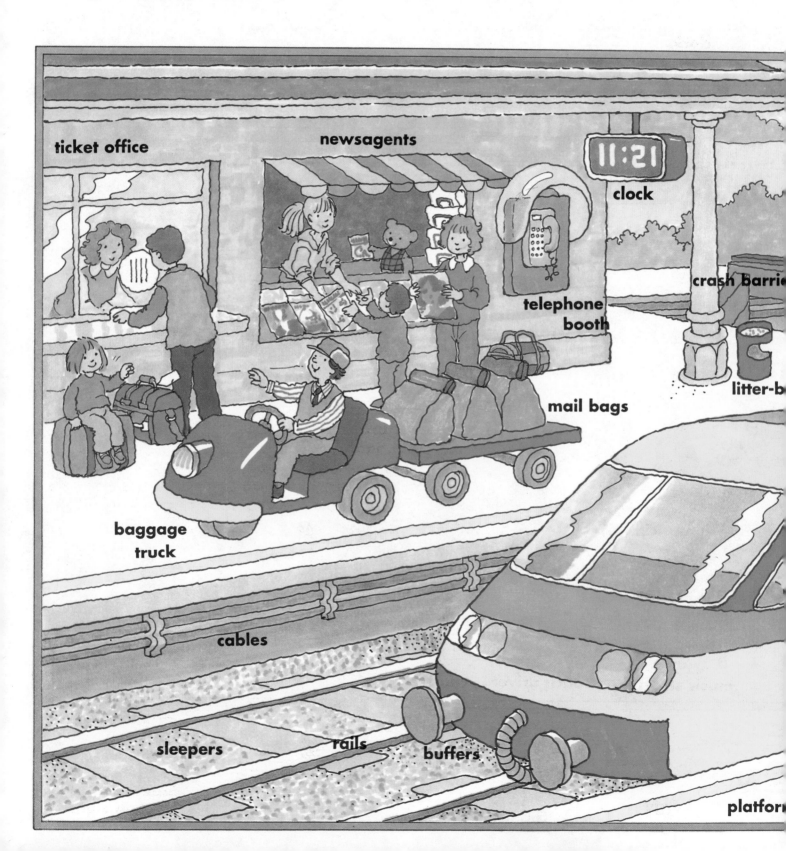

ticket office

newsagents

clock

telephone booth

crash barrier

litter-b

mail bags

baggage truck

cables

sleepers

rails

buffers

platform

driver

taxi

steam

tanker

hopper

coal

steam engine

seat

passengers

carriage

Diesel engine

train-spotter

driver

passenger

newspaper

ticket kiosk

handbag

briefcase

guard

ticket collector

suitcase

hold-all

# At the airport

The airport was huge and extremely busy. Tom and Susie were very excited.

First their luggage was weighed and their tickets checked at the desk.

After the security check Tom said he was hungry. "Don't worry," laughed Mum, "the air hostess will bring you lunch on the plane."

tow tractor

computer

baggage trolley

ambulance

pilot

baggage truck

marshal

security check

air hostess

information screen

fuel truck

check-in

security check

lunchtime

baggage claim

**jet liner**

**landing gear**

**hangar**

**jet engine**

**control tower**

**mechanic**

**walkway**

**loader**

**Concorde**

**take-off**

**runway**

**loading**

palm tree

sea

motor-yacht

yacht

winch

sail

pedalo

wind-surfer

hats

gift-seller

rowing boat

gravel    flowers

## The holiday at the beach

The Cherry family arrived at their hotel later in the day.

The sea was warm and a beautiful blue. The sun was very hot and everyone had to buy a shady hat.

Tom and Susie couldn't wait to dive into the swimming pool while Mum and Dad sat in the sun.

hat

jug

drink

sunbed

dinghy

palm tree

motor-boat

sunglasses

sun-cream

lifebelt

jet-ski

# A visit to the harbour

While Tom and Susie were away on holiday, Monty was having a wonderful time with Grandma and Grandpa.

One day they took him to visit the harbour. Monty was very excited by all the strange sights and smells.

He watched the fishermen unloading their catch of fish, and he saw a very big ship getting ready to sail to a

warehouses

passenger ship

van

lorry

crane

harbour wall

anchor

diver

helmet

jetty

rowing boat

tug-boat

steps

mast

radar

air-hose

oar

winch

hold

funne

boxes

deck-house

fisherman

truck

forklift truck

cat

fish boxes

fish

faraway place.

He barked at a seagull that tried to peck him on the nose, and fell into the water. Luckily for Monty, Grandpa was holding tightly onto his lead!

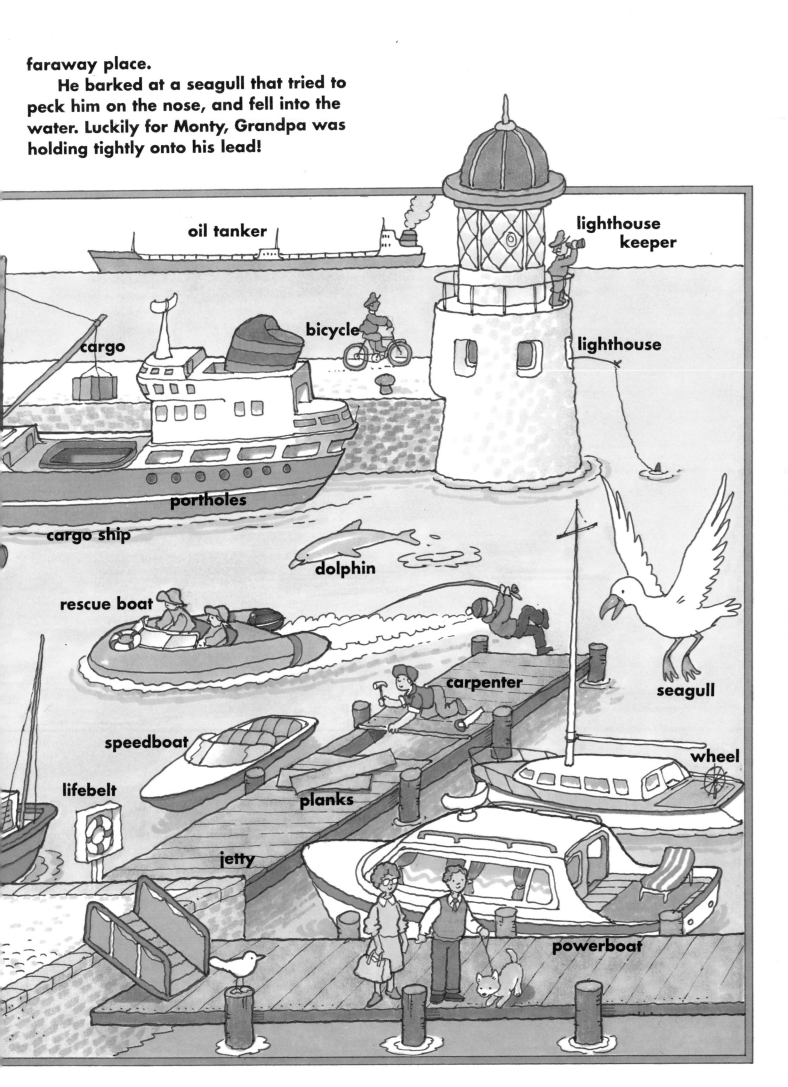

oil tanker

lighthouse keeper

cargo

bicycle

lighthouse

portholes

cargo ship

dolphin

rescue boat

carpenter

seagull

speedboat

wheel

lifebelt

planks

jetty

powerboat

Here is a list of words you can learn about 'Going on hoilday.'

## a
irline
ant
antelope
ant-hill
anteater
avalanche
anorak
ambulance
anchor
air-hose
air hostess

## b
ikini
bathing trunks
bandage
batteries
box
biscuits
blanket
brush
brochures
beauty case
basket
backpack
bell tower
barge
baskets
band
banner
beaver
boulders
bridge
bear
bush hat
binoculars
bananas
butterfly
banana plant
beak
buffalo
bush helmet
bili
baggage truck
buffers
briefcase
baggage trolley
balcony
beach
bicycle
boxes
beach-ball
bucket
bobsleigh team

bill

## c
ardigan
cap
credit card
chocolate
comic
carpenter
camera
cassette
comb
collar
computer
calculator
carpet
camera bag
cloud
castle
clock
cruise ship
coach
cobbles
coach driver
courier
clarinet
camera
camping stove
canoe
cheetah
chimpanzee
clay pots
crocodile
cable
cable-car
chalet
church
coal
crash-barrier
clock
cables
carriage
control tower
Concorde
cloud
cargo
crane
cargo ship
cat
cliff
cave
car
can
cool box
cake
claws
cold drinks
chair lift

## d
ress

dog basket
desk
drinks
dog
downhill racer
driver
diesel engine
driver
drink
dinghy
diving
diver
deck-house
dolphin
deck chair

## e
lephant
elephant calf

## f
lipflops
foreign money
first-aid box
film
food bowl
flight bag
flower basket
flower stall
folding stool
fish
fisherman
fishing rod
frying pan
ferns
flamingo
flag
finish
forest
fuel tanker
fir-tree
fishing boat
flowers
forklift truck
funnel
fish boxes
footprints
flask
flippers
face mask
fishing-net

## g
ame
grass
gazelle
goggles
glove
guard
gravel
gift-seller
giraffe

## h
eadphones
hold-all
hotel sign
house-boat
hiking boots
hornbill
hut
hippopotamus
horn
hyena
helmet
hood
hotel
handbag
hangar
hat
harbour wall
hold
horizon
harbour
hopper

## i
ron
ironing
ironing-board
island
ice-cream van
ice-cream
instructor
information screen

## j
eans
jeep
jet liner
jet-ski
jet engine
jug
jetty

## k
nickers
knot
keyboard
kettle
kite
kayak

## l
aces
leggings
lead
landing stage
life-jacket
lake
litter
litter basket
log cabins
lion cub
lioness
lion